The Art of F

Polly Hall

www.pollyhall.co.uk

The Art of Foot Reading

by Polly Hall

First Edition 2009

Published by Polly Hall

9 Clover Way

Highbridge

Somerset

TA9 3LL

United Kingdom

www.pollyhall.co.uk

ISBN: 978-0-9563652-0-0

Illustrations by Polly Hall

Foot Map illustrations by Claire Hargrave

Contents

What is Foot Reading?

How can you read a foot? Well in some respects foot reading is exactly what is says, the foot can be read like a book. It is not the same as palm reading because there is no element of divination involved but visual clues can prompt the reader as to what is going on with that person, at that particular time.

Foot Reading is a natural assistant to reflexology and other therapies involving the feet. Reflexologists, while not claiming to diagnose in the medical sense, can discern what imbalances there are in the body by looking at and touching the feet. Foot Reading extends this skill by viewing each individual as an emotional, mental and spiritual being as well as made up of physical parts.

Foot Reading is closely linked with reflexology. Reflexology is a therapy that involves specific massage of the reflex points of the feet that correspond to that persons' body and has been found to relieve many acute and chronic conditions. Like reflexology, Foot Reading concentrates on the representation of the person on the feet, in effect the foot is seen as a microcosm of the whole self.

Reflexology foot charts often place only the physical body parts onto the foot reflex areas, for example; the head area is mapped onto the toes; the chest area on the ball of the foot; the digestive system on the instep and the pelvic/reproductive area on the heels with the inner and outer skeletal system on the sides of the feet.

Foot Reading takes this theory further and looks at the markings, shape, size and colour of the feet and applies these signs and indicators at a deeper level, concentrating on emotional, mental and perceptual patterns that are relevant to that person's life.

Largely an intuitive tool, Foot Reading, can be learnt by anyone willing to study it. Insight into what a person is like will become clear using visual cues on the feet and interpreting them as 'signs and indicators'.

Inherent personality traits can also be read from the feet. For example, a wide sturdy foot normally belongs to a hard-working, practical person, not afraid to get physically stuck in. Whereas a narrow, slender foot belongs to a person who enjoys being pampered and treated like royalty! This isn't to say that the way the person lives their life reflects this fully as other signs and markings can indicate if they are being true to their nature or not.

Some women can wear a pair of stilettos all day, everyday and not get a single blister yet some women will buy a fancy pair of shoes for a special occasion and end up in agony after wearing them for only one night. This reflects the true nature of the person via their feet, because the woman who feels comfortable being herself in high heels is comfortable in the footwear she has chosen whereas the woman who chooses some shoes for an occasion to fit in to what society says she must wear, is going against her true nature and her feet will tell her this in no uncertain terms. Normally in a painful way, resulting in blisters or aching arches.

Apart from the shape and size of feet, the position of the feet and toes can indicate forward thinking or past issues weighing down on that persons subconscious. These may be issues to do with home and security, relationships, work or emotions. It is this subconscious reflection that is most interesting because it is hidden from view, just like the soles of the feet. It is no strange coincidence that the sole of the foot mirrors the 'soul' of the person. Motivations and often hidden behaviour can be seen when reading the soles of the feet and the position of the toes.

Foot Reading can be used as a stand alone technique to relay useful information back to someone about their own life and strategies for living. It is largely an intuitive skill that is developed over time but once the basics are known it is relatively easy to apply.

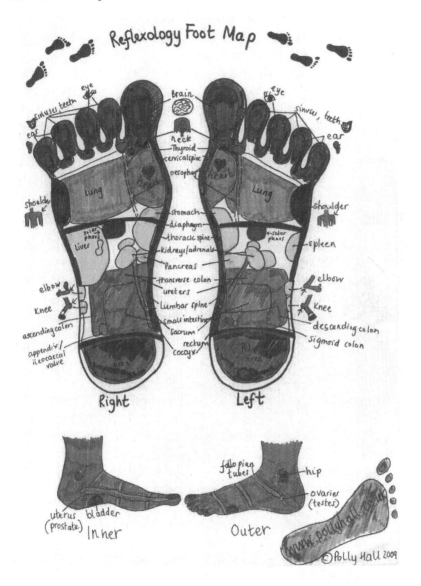

Reflexology Foot Map

Origins of Foot Reading

Foot Reading has its basis in modern reflexology but the synthesis between the feet and body has been charted for centuries, dating as far back to ancient Egypt and China.

In fact, the origins of Foot Reading if linked with reflexology have their foundations in emerging science and are not as alternative as some might think. William Fitzgerald, a prominent ear, nose and throat surgeon studied the analgesic effects of applying pressure to the hands while performing surgery. This connection was later to be studied in more detail by his assistant Eunice Ingham, now known as the mother of reflexology, whereby she mapped out the reflex points onto the feet in relation to the human body.

The correlating influences of the mind and emotions on the physical body are well documented in medical science also. A positive attitude is widely regarded as having a healing effect on the body. Likewise the power of the mind is evident in the placebo effect, so named after the mock medication prescribed in place of actual drugs to treat a specified condition. This highlights the complex relationship of mind and body and the reality imposed by an individual to determine how they feel. The subjective experience is just as valid evidence as any objective study.

There has not always been such a skew of favour towards symptomatic medicine or objectivism in science. In fact the father of modern medicine Hippocrates was a great advocate of holistic approaches. With centres set up to analyse dreams and offer massage and hydrotherapy in ancient Greece he recognised the need to embrace all aspects of a person in terms of their personality and outlook and how that would shape their susceptibility to ailments. Treating the cause rather than the symptom is the main preface of most complementary therapies rather than reactionary approaches to eliminate only symptoms.

Gaston St Pierre, a pioneer of the Metamorphic Technique explains this representation of the body on the feet as the principle of correspondence. Everything is interconnected and with this knowledge it is clear to see how all things reflect everything else. Every living being is made of the same essence, and that is energy. So in our form as human beings we contain boundless potential and yet most of us are never aware of it. The feet are said to be the moving centre in metamorphosis so are the key to transformation taking place. So by employing them in Foot Reading we are openly allowing this process by interacting with another who can reflect back what that person is like.

Imre Somogyi, concentrates on the toes and specialises in Toe Reading. Each toe represents our perceptions of various aspects of our character. The position, shape and relation to other toes are read for that individual along with markings and flexibility. He uses case studies to demonstrate this approach in a startlingly accurate way when assessing the personality patterns of individuals previously unknown to him.

The interconnectness of the universe is celebrated by leading holistic teachers such as William Bloom, Louise Hay and Chris Stormer.

Chris Stormer, pioneered Foot Reading with her findings in 'Language of the Feet' detailing the meanings of the foot's shapes, textures, colours and markings relative to their location and position. For example, hard skin over the throat reflex can mean on a physical level, throat problems or susceptibility to weakness in this area of the body; on an emotional level it suggests a barrier to speaking what one feels creating a blockage in the throat energy centre or chakra.

It is her work that has laid the foundations for the modern Foot Reader and holistic therapist. Yet it is not an altogether new age idea. The synthesis between mind, body and spirit has been investigated, studied and revered for as long as man has lived. By application of how the different modalities interact, the individual is more able to connect why certain emotions can manifest and relate to physical conditions or even exacerbate them.

Benefits of Foot Reading

How can Foot Reading help? Surely a person knows himself don't they? Why do they need to be told what they are like or who they are? And what benefit can they gain from such a bizarre experience as someone looking at their feet?

These are some questions that may be asked of Foot Reading. However, the answer is simple, the benefits go far beyond the realms of a simple conversation with another, it is as if you are allowed to read that persons soul, quite literally (sole equals soul). And by letting you in to their 'inner world' a portal is opened to reveal greater insight than if a person pondered introspectively.

The act of revealing one's feet is sacred and sensitive even in the most liberal of societies. Ask anyone about their feet and they will rarely be indifferent. They will state that they 'love them' or 'hate them' or indeed 'hate all things to do with feet'. They will pull faces or exclaim that they can think of nothing they want more than someone to touch their feet. Feet are like mini-me's full of information about that person.

The ability to be open-minded and use intuition are pre-requisites when reading feet, this is because you never know what you will be faced with when someone sheds their shoes and socks.

The daintiest of creatures may reveal the largest, cumbersome feet or the apparent hard-edged thug may turn out to be soft and delicate underneath his worldly facade. The feet will never lie; they cannot, as they are the true representation of that person.

Some of the benefits of Foot Reading for the recipient include:

- *Empowerment through awareness of the self*

- *Reflecting upon the words and descriptions used in the Foot Reading to assess current patterns and traits*

- *Positive feedback to help self-development*

- *Personal perceptions – a view of how others see you is important for personal growth*

- *A holistic add-on to many therapies, in particular reflexology*

- *An alternative way of viewing your 'self'*

The increase in popularity of natural therapies arises largely from the inability to find relief from physical ailments in symptomatic medication alone. Drugs, alcohol, food and smoking may provide temporary relief from some symptoms but cannot address the emotive causes unless a conscious change of attitude occurs also.

By using learned knowledge of how feet reflect our subconscious and unconscious patterns, we can release ourselves from unhealthy thoughts and behaviour.

How do you feel about your feet today? Do you like them? Hate them? Don't think about them too much? Do they feel tired or sore?

To ask someone how they feel about their feet is to ask how they feel about their 'self'. The feet can reveal our subconscious and act as a reflection of our self too.

> ## EXERCISE: TUNING IN TO YOUR FEET
>
> *Sit quietly.*
>
> *Close your eyes and bring your attention to your feet.*
>
> *Start at your toes then the balls of your feet, your insteps and your heels. Then your ankles and all over the tops of your feet. Sink back into your soles.*
>
> *Notice how they feel including things like temperature, tension, position, relation to each other.*
>
> *Now open your eyes and have a good look at your feet, top and bottom, instep, sole, toes, nails and so on.*
>
> *Now write 3 words to describe your feet.*
>
> *Reflect upon these words in relation to how you are feeling about your 'self'.*

This first impression allows the Foot Reader to gauge the mind set of the individual and put themselves in another's shoes! By reflecting back to someone how they are perceived by the outside world is a very powerful technique and must always be carried out with care.

This is an essential part of the Foot Reading because the purpose is to empower the person to know their 'self' more fully and in doing so effect a positive change. This may manifest at a subtle level or consciously effect a change in behaviour or attitude because of this new awareness. Therefore the benefits can be far reaching for the individual.

You might like to use the foot template to note how you feel about specific parts of your feet or using coloured pencils/pens can be useful here. Be as creative as you like, use symbols, colours, shapes, words, images to depict your feelings.

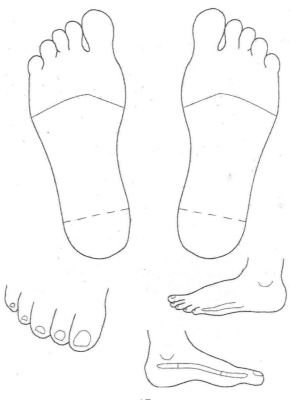

What is the point of Foot Reading? Aside from being an interesting conversation starter, it mostly can be used alongside treatments involving the feet, like reflexology, to get a broader perspective of that person's thoughts, feelings and motivations. Most important of all it can allow self-empowerment by encouraging a healthy look at what is true to the self and what is not, thereby offering a route to positive change.

Foot Reading is emotive for the recipient and involves no special powers or psychic abilities. It is simple to learn and easy to practice providing you have access to lots of feet! What is reflected in a person's feet is deeply sensitive and important to them, so feedback should be given with tact and diplomacy. Never blurt out something unless you are sure how it will be received and if the intended message is for that person's highest good.

Reflexologists may wish to learn Foot Reading as an additional skill to advance their understanding of clients' needs and offer a more holistic perspective.

You don't need any previous knowledge of reflexology or therapy to read the feet but it is best to start by reading your own feet. Until you know yourself and can relate what you find on your feet it is difficult to authentically describe what you find on others feet. A basic one day Foot Reading workshop will equip you with this knowledge and with dedication, experience and practice you can become an accomplished Foot Reader.

Using Intuition

Intuition is a natural tool and always works best when you trust it. Defined as pure, untaught, direct perception of knowing, it is difficult to teach how it feels. Some describe it as gut instinct or that immediate clear knowing that just 'feels right'. There is no specific or right way of accessing your intuition but each person will find what works best for them. Regular meditation is thought to be a good way of heightening this ability.

You might like to try some of these exercises to help engage your intuition and the right side of the brain. The right side of the brain is associated with the more creative, intuitive thoughts and concepts like colour, imagination, daydreaming, rhythm and images.

EXERCISE: RELEASE YOUR INNER CHILD

You will need lots of colouring pens, a black marker pen and some paper.

Draw a shape onto the paper – it can be abstract, straight lines, curvy – anything you desire.

Divide it up using your black marker pen to make shapes within the larger space. Then choose colours to fill in all the spaces.

Notice how you feel as you carry out this exercise but above all just enjoy the experience of colouring in.

EXERCISE: COLOUR PREDICTION

Using coloured scarves or balls place them in a dark bag so you can't see them.

Intend to select a specific colour and reach into the bag.

It is your intention that is most important here so be clear about what colour you wish to select.

Go with what feels right and keep practicing until you can select the colour you are focusing on.

Something that is unlikely to happen has a probability of less than half so if you predict 10 colours and select 6 or more correctly your intuition is higher than average.

You can do this exercise with shapes on cards, pictures of people, animals or objects. Be inventive and stretch yourself to improve your intuition.

EXERCISE: THE CHOSEN ONE

This is a group exercise to practice using intuition. This works best with 4 or more people. You will need a pen and paper.

Select a person to be 'the chosen one'.

The person who is 'the chosen one' will go to one room and the others will decide who will visit them in the other room in a certain order. They will then give 'the chosen one' 5 minutes to write down the order first.

Remember you are only practicing so make a note of the order then discuss afterwards any feelings, or gut instincts 'the chosen one' may have had.

If you don't have another room improvise with space, i.e. turn their chair to face away from the group and decide who will walk round 'the chosen one's' chair in a specific order.

EXERCISE: TUNING INTO BELONGINGS

This is known as psychometry, a branch of intuition that allows someone to pick up details about someone else from their belongings.

Ideally you will need an object that means something or is familiar to you and perhaps has a story or person attached to it. i.e. a piece of jewellery handed down in the family, or a gift from a friend.

The person tuning in will need to hold the object and close their eyes. Then they can write down or tell the owner what they pick up.

Try to include all your senses, do you visualise something or someone, is there a fragrance that is evident, perhaps a sound or some music comes to mind, or a feeling?

The owner of the object will be able to verify the thoughts and feelings you describe in relation to the object.

Intuition can be referred to as a sixth sense and by using all the other five senses you are allowing synthesis. Find what works best for you.

First Impressions

We use expressions in our language to describe someone related to their feet, for example, 'he is light on his feet' or 'she put her foot in it' or 'he's always tripping up' or 'tread lightly with her'. These foot metaphors all have their basis in our observations of what we think a person is like.

Initial impressions are usually instinctively correct and foot shapes are a starting point when reading the feet as they contain the overall information needed about dominant personality traits.

When we analyse feet we see them from many different perspectives. From an intuitive angle we can ask what brings that person to us, what is their physical posture saying, how do they act when revealing their feet? People may come to you wearing a mask which is not real to them. When we examine their feet we are able to see what is behind the mask or inside their subconscious.

The size of the feet will reflect the congruence of the potential of the person and can be assessed in relation to their body physique. For example, a petite person with large feet can use tremendous energy if they tread carefully, they may also feel inhibited or embarrassed by their large feet as they don't match up with the rest of their body.

Short feet = likes to assume a background role, sometimes shy or not really bothered if they go unnoticed

Long feet = likes to project themselves to others, centre of attention, confident when they know their subject well

Pretty feet = likes to be pampered, feels great benefit from relaxation and attention

Angular feet = could be perceived as quite unique or sometimes difficult to get on with

Chunky feet = down to earth, practical, more concerned with the everyday aspects of living

The arches of the feet on the medial edge are associated with the spinal reflexes and so are related to interdependence and support.

High arches = high level of independence, prefers time on their own to assess their life and energy levels, finds it difficult to accept outside help

Fallen arches = a sudden need for support from others leading to a dependent state, can manifest as backache or pain in knees

Low or flat arches = likes to have support of other people, to be around others to feel secure

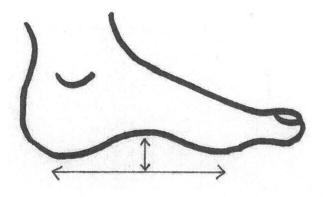

The front of the foot or dorsum is what is shown to the world and the sole is the hidden self. Look for differences between the dorsum and sole to decipher how well the person conceals their inner self.

Left foot = feminine traits, intuitive, present issues

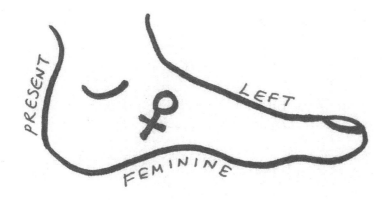

Right foot = masculine traits, logical, past issues

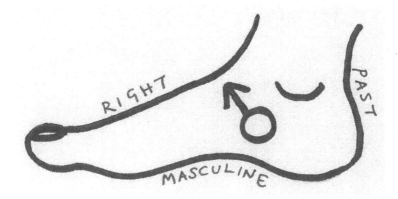

Elements

One part of reading the feet is by looking at the elemental aspect of our human nature as portrayed by the seasons, nature and the balance of matter through air, fire, water, earth and ether.

History and origin of the elements

Air, Fire, Water and Earth are the basic constituents of life. Empedocles, an ancient Greek philosopher wrote of these four classical elements that exist and co-exist in all matter. The diagram of a square upon a square shows the corners of one as the classical elements, air, fire, earth and water and the corners of the other as their properties. Air as wet and hot; Fire as hot and dry; Earth as dry and cold; and Water as cold and wet.

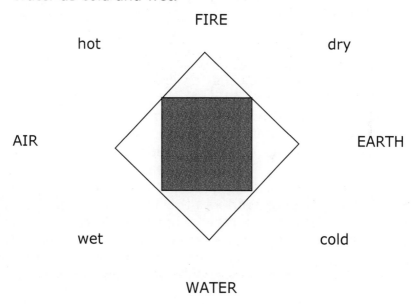

FIRE

hot   dry

AIR   EARTH

wet   cold

WATER

27

Elements and their Properties

Hippocrates later described the body as consisting of four humours, blood, yellow bile, phlegm and black bile and applied the elements in a medical context relating to these. The predominant fluid was used to define the type of personality and a fluctuation or diminishment in these fluids would result in symptoms or behaviour dominant to that fluid's characteristics.

Blood as hot/wet most characterised the sanguine person who displayed as happy and warm. Yellow bile as hot/dry most characterised the choleric type who displayed as angry and vengeful. Phlegm as cold/wet most characterised the phlegmatic personality who displayed as placid and lethargic. Black bile as cold/dry most characterised the melancholic type who displayed as the name implies, sad or melancholic.

The imbalance of these four humours was thought to lead to the cause of illness in the body. Galen greatly influenced this as a medical theory for many years until the mid 1800's when cellular pathology displaced its popularity. Symptomatic interpretation of disease is still used widely in mainstream medicine but the increasing trend of complementary and alternative medicine has encouraged investigation into the 'cause' of illness rather than just treating the 'symptoms'. The interrelationship of aspects of the human being i.e. mind, body and spirit and their effect on health and well-being is a core foundation of all holistic therapies.

The elements emerge from subtle to dense, high to low, external to introspective and show on the feet from the toes to the heel, air to earth. When the four elements are applied to the four distinct areas of the foot, the dominant and submissive parts of the individual are revealed. The foot can be divided into four distinct parts, the toes; the ball of the foot; the instep; and the heel and the elements of air, fire, water and earth can be applied to these parts of the foot.

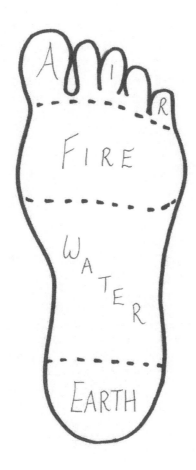

AIR = TOES

The toes are representative of the air element, reaching upwards and associated with the brain and sensory organs of the head. The element of air is limitless, standing for truth, purity, integrity and expression. Too little air will mean suffocation and restriction, too much air leads to detachment and ungrounding.

FIRE – BALL OF FOOT

The ball of the foot represents the element of fire, abundant and expansive in the reflex areas of the heart, lungs and shoulders. The element of fire is bright and vibrant like intense passion and desire, spreading quickly, unrestricted in its movement. Too little oxygen or fuel and fire cannot survive, too much fire can be destructive and out of control.

WATER - INSTEP

The instep shows the water element, often the largest section, covering the digestive system and internal organs. Humans are 70% water and cannot survive without it. The element of water can take many forms just as our emotions do, when controlled it can be cleansing and renewing, when stirred or unmanaged it can be dangerous or stagnant.

EARTH - HEEL

The heel as the earth element, in contact with the ground, strong and sturdy like the bony pelvic area and reproductive system representing foundations for growth and nurturing. The element of earth is secure and steady, solid enough to hold all the other elements. When nurtured and respected the fertile earth is naturally abundant and productive. When agitated, shattering earthquakes can occur. If our foundations like the element of earth are shattered or destroyed we are unsteady on our feet, left ungrounded and unstable.

Reading the Elements on the Feet

These will provide clues to that person's main traits and motivations and what is central to their core being.

Questions to ask include:

- Ask if they have a favourite part of their foot what would it be – this gives an indication of the element they are most in tune with at that time.
- What is the largest proportion of their foot when divided into the four main sections? This will give a clue to the dominant core elemental traits.
- What is the smallest proportion of their foot when divided into the four main sections? This will give a clue to the least core dominant elemental traits.
- What other signs and indicators are there e.g. colour, texture, marks, temperature?
- Are the elements completely distinct or is there an overlap?
- Is there conflict within an element section? e.g. look at the texture, colour, any markings etc.
- Is there a synergy between two or more elements?

Dominant traits of the four elements

AIR	expression & intuition; perceptive and mentally agile
FIRE	passion & desire; confident and talented
WATER	emotion & self-worth; sensitive and flexible
EARTH	stability & security; hard-working and realistic

Looking at the elements is only one part of reading the feet and should be analysed with other indicators as well.

EXERCISE: WORKING WITH THE ELEMENTS

Tune in to your feet

Is there an area of your feet that you feel most drawn to today? (note: this can change)

Try to discern if this is:

- *Toes*
- *Ball of foot*
- *Instep*
- *Heel*

This will be the element you are focusing on at this present moment.

For the following elemental areas you can try some of the following to encourage re-balancing:

Toes = AIR: take 3 deep breaths in through the nose and out through the mouth while stretching the arms up above the head.

Stretch, pull and rotate each toe while concentrating on your in and out breath.

Ball of foot = FIRE: stand hip width apart and gently rock onto the balls of your feet, one at a time and then both together. Breathe in and out in rhythm with your rocking motion.

Instep = WATER: use a golf ball or similar round object. Sit well supported and one foot at a time roll it under the instep applying as much or little pressure as you want. Let the water element flow in and out as you breathe deep into your belly.

Heel = EARTH: walk on your heels then stamp your feet one at a time or bounce up and down. Connect to the earth. Remember to breathe deeply as you stamp.

Past/Present/Future

The position of the feet shows the overall focus of that person at that given time. This is shown in the direction they point when in a prone, relaxed position i.e. when they put their feet up in front of you.

So if the feet are facing you remember that their left is on your right and vice versa.

This can change many times during a Foot Reading session as the person responds and reflects on the information they are receiving.

When reading the signs and indicators you will see that the left and right foot are often different. The right foot represents the past and what has influenced them, sometimes going back many years, and the left foot shows the present or current issues that are being worked out.

Past – the right foot represents the past and its influences. If the feet are leaning towards their right side then the subconscious is drawing them back to resolve past issues.

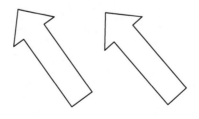

Present – upright feet show a focus on the present moment. They are neither weighed down by the past or concerned by the future.

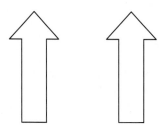

Future – if the feet are leaning towards the left side then the focus is to be somewhere else than the present, they are rushing forward to the next task or even in the distant future.

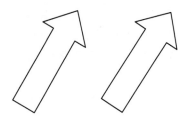

Signs and Indicators

More detailed observations found on the feet and include:

- **Shape**
- **Colour**
- **Temperature**
- **Tone**
- **Texture**

Shape of Feet	Meaning
Broad	Capable, down to earth, hard working, organised and methodical. Can sometimes put their foot in it!
Narrow	Gentle, sensitive type. Enjoys being pampered.
Straight	Straight forward approach to life. Need to be cautious about being too direct.
Squashed	Constrained and suppressed to conform with others beliefs. Lack of individuality.
Mixed	Diverse qualities.
Misshapen	Given in to relentless pressure. Moulded to suit others beliefs. Need to rediscover own self.
Swollen	Unhappy. Weighed down with unresolved emotions.
Flat	Total dependence on others for support.
Unblemished	Adapts and goes with the flow. Forever hopeful and positive.

Shape of Feet	Meaning
Floppy	Not able to stand up for self. Needs to boost self esteem.
Flexible	Adapts easily to lifes ups and downs. If too flexible, easily manipulated.
Rigid	Harsh, strict, principled, precise.
Heavy	Weighed down, burdened by unresolved emotions. Need to release.
Ticklish	Concerned about others opinions & feelings.
Physical (large soles, small insignif. toes)	No time for thoughts or imagination as demands of physical world takes over.
Philosophical (big toes/big pads)	Head full of ideas, good business acumen. Capable of vigorous, decisive activity.
Psychic/intuitive (long toe necks)	Head in clouds, little concern for physical world. Dreamers.

Examples:

- Inward turning feet are often found on introspective people prone to looking deep within themselves almost to the exclusion of others. People with autism for example; demonstrate this characteristic via their feet and their demeanour.

- Bunions are a big giveaway that the owner of them bends over backwards to help others, often to the detriment of themselves.

Skin colour	Meaning
Flesh	Healthy, confident, balanced
Pale	Drained of energy, washed out, trying too hard
Red	Embarrassed, self conscious, passionate, angry
Yellow/orange	Totally fed up. Resentful, indignant, displeased.
Blue/purple	Injured pride, bruised ego, battered self-esteem. Be kind to self!
Green	Extreme bitterness, envy, discontent. Look for the good!
Brown	Browned off, bored, fed up.
Black marks	Deep emotional stabs. Perceived difficulty. Need to trust process of life.
White dots	Eruption of unexpressed emotions like anger, jealousy & frustration.

Examples:

- Yellow, hard skin on the shoulder reflex (below 5th toes) shows tension and resentment relating to responsibilities, can feel burdened at having to take it all on by oneself.

- Pale dusty skin on the digestive reflex (instep) shows a giving out of too much energy from the emotional self resulting in depletion.

- White dots on the brain reflex (big toe) shows unexpressed thoughts that recurrently play on the mind.

Temperature	Meaning
Warm	Glowing with temperate energy
Burning	Inflamed, angry, passionate , excited
Cold	Demotivated, unenthusiastic, weakened

Examples:

- Look for temperature changes which can show where the energy is stagnant or overactive.

- Hot heels denote impatience and burning desire to get on with something.

- Cold toes may show that person is working on autopilot and not really being mindful about their thoughts.

Skin tone & texture	Represents:	Action
Soft & pliable	Easy going, adapts spontaneously & responds appropriately	Be yourself!
Excessively soft	Potentially hesitant and lazy. Enjoys voluptuous pleasure.	Requires inner strength.
Flaccid	Gives up easily. No enthusiasm or strength.	Needs to be more resolute.

Skin tone & texture	Represents:	Action
Oedema	Overburdened. Filled with unresolved burdens that inhibit and weigh down.	Need to unshackle self.
Hardened	Protective, defensive, stubborn, adamant. Concealing something.	Needs a more relaxed approach.
Sensitive	Easily hurt. Vulnerable, self-conscious, impressionable.	Requires inner security.
Shiny	Worn away. Reflecting back emotions in hope that others will be more understanding. Emotional friction from rubbing against perceived barriers.	Need to feel secure and less categorical.
Rough	Having a strained, stormy, disorderly, harsh time.	A level head and calm mind needed to soothe path.
Flaking	Extreme irritability at others or circumstances. 'getting under the skin'	Need for change. To be more tolerant to self & others.
Athletes foot	Ideas perceivably rejected causing much irritation & frustration.	Requires acknowledgement & recognition.
Fragile	Delicate, easily hurt.	Needs to boost self-esteem.
Smooth & dry	Exposed feelings, quick to take offence.	Needs more relaxed approach to ease the way.
Blistered	Friction, inner burning that has surfaced.	Be kind to yourself.

Skin tone & texture	Represents:	Action
Wrinkled	Troubled and drained. Sapped of energy	Stop worrying about self & others.
Thick and hard	Thick skinned. Insensitive, strong willed with argumentative streak.	Be less dependent on physical aspects of life.
Rubbery or plastic	Lacking zest or vitality. Vulnerable esp during periods of exposure or uncertainty.	Embrace the newness of change.
Callouses	Emotional barriers (see related part). Extreme vulnerability.	Need to go with flow and believe in self.
Peeling	Extreme agitation.	Allow layers to peel for fresh start.
Cracked	Divided and torn apart (see related part)	Need to trust the process of life.
Deep crevices	Feeling cut up or divided	Go with the flow.
Blood capilliaries	Inner emotional turmoil & grief coming to surface.	Release with love & understanding.
Prominent bulging capillaries	Subconscious hurts and unresolved issues need to be released.	Be kind to yourself.
Sores	Fresh hurts & open wounds	Take time to heal.
Wounds	Old injuries leaving their mark	Accept the past as part of you.
Scars	Remnants of past pain, memory of which often concealed.	Accept the past as part of you.

Skin tone & texture	Represents:	Action
Verrucas	Extreme frustration at resources being tapped.	Needs to be more resourceful.
Dirt	Covers true vulnerability & self-conciousness. Hiding, feeling dirty.	Wash away wasteful emotions.
Fluff/Debri	Extra loads that are dispensable.	Get rid – not needed!
Temporary marks	Fleeting impressions	Useful but should not be taken seriously.
Itchy	Irritatable, deep yearning to move on	Action will eradicate the itchiness.
Swelling and lumps	Accumulated emotional congestion	Express yourself through talking about your feelings or writing them down.

Examples:

- Fleshy liver area – lot of contained energy and anger that has been stored for a long time.

- Lines on bowel – processing everything and inside that more to be processed. A worrier.

- Smooth bowel – processed emotions and able to deal with life.

- Scratches on the heel – struggles for safety; for physiological needs, money or work.

- Ripples on heel – worry from a harsh change in life e.g. break up of relationship, loss of loved one, breakdown.

- Hard skin on throat reflex (neck of big toes) = built up protection from having to swallow undesirable verbal communication. Conceals true expression.

- Flaking skin over hard skin on pelvic reflex (heels) = irritated at having to protect and justify movements. Heels relate to security for growth, movement and development.

- Dry skin in the heart area – a barrier in the giving and receiving process with others and also themselves.

- Dry skin in the lungs area – pollution (could be related to physical effects of a respiratory problem), also as an analogy of accepting air or spirit. The way in which you accept the universe or deal with your own environment. Also how does the person accept themselves as part of the universe?

- Dry skin on oesophagus – area related to swallowing new experiences, fearful of trusting and believing.

Chakras on the Feet

The seven major chakras or energy centres can be placed on the foot. The position of the chakras are shown from toes down to heels and are as follows.

Crown and Third Eye Chakras

Physical aspect	Head area; sinuses; teeth; eyes; ears; brain
Emotional aspect	Perceptions of subconscious and unconscious mind
Mental aspect	Awareness and thought patterns; verbal expression
Spiritual aspect	Potential to manifest thoughts
Element	Ether & Air
Part of foot	Toes
Colour	Violet & Indigo

Throat Chakra

Physical aspect	Throat; thyroid; neck; jaw
Emotional aspect	Perceptions verbalizing your feelings
Mental aspect	Manifested ideas spoken out loud
Spiritual aspect	Speaking your truth
Element	Ether & Air & Fire
Part of foot	Neck of big toe
Colour	Blue

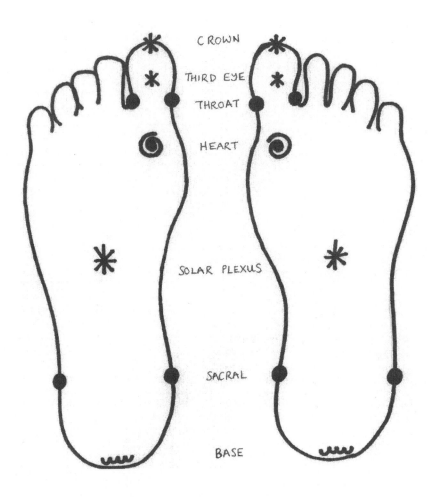

CROWN

THIRD EYE

THROAT

HEART

SOLAR PLEXUS

SACRAL

BASE

Heart Chakra

Physical aspect	Heart, lungs, thyroid, oesophagus, shoulders, diaphragm
Emotional aspect	Perceptions of giving & receiving, self-worth, compassion and love
Mental aspect	Responsibilities or burdens, ideas and approach to life, swallowing experiences
Spiritual aspect	Acting intuitively and with stability, central core of being
Element	Fire
Part of foot	Balls of feet
Colour	Green

Solar Plexus

Physical aspect	Liver, kidneys, spleen, pancreas, stomach, digestive system, solar plexus
Emotional aspect	Perceptions of coping with life's experiences, gut feelings, personal safety and power
Mental aspect	Assimilation of changing mood patterns, support needed, independence, management of emotions
Spiritual aspect	Free flowing, movement of self-expression,
Element	Water
Part of foot	Solar Plexus
Colour	Yellow

Sacral and Base Chakras

Physical aspect	Reproductive system; hips; pelvis
Emotional aspect	Feeling secure and stable
Mental aspect	Motivation and mobilization of thoughts and ideas;
Spiritual aspect	Grounding and in touch with the material world so a firm base to build and grow
Element	Earth
Part of foot	Heel
Colour	Orange and Red

Toes

Our toes reflect our thoughts and perceptions and each toe has an individual meaning related to beliefs, feelings, action, relationships and motivation. It is the toe size, position and shape that can reflect how our perceptions interrelate and any changes that are currently showing or have been relevant in the past.

Characteristics are often evident in groups of people with similar interests or careers. For example, people with backgrounds involving strong motivational leadership styles or the ability to manage others and set the pace will have 2nd toes longer than the other toes especially the big toe. If this is not channelled fully the characteristic will forcibly present itself and they may be perceived as being bossy.

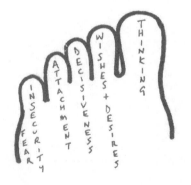

Meanings of the toes

	RIGHT (male)	LEFT (female)	ELEMENT
Big Toe	Thinking	Thinking	Ether
2nd Toe	Wishes & Desires	Emotions	Air
3rd Toe	Aggression & Decision Making	Creativity	Fire
4th Toe	Attachments	Love	Water
5th Toe	Fear & Security	Trust, Sex, Optimism	Earth

Energies of the toes

Each toe is connected to an element in the five zones of each foot. All the energies will come out via the ether element as represented by the big toe so the position of the big toe to the other toes is quite important.

Looking at an imaginary line from the 5th toe to the big toe we can determine if the big toe is shorter or longer. If shorter then energies are lost as the person tries to express the multitude of feelings, or go from one subject to another while doing something else.

If the big toe is longer then there is a lot of talk, in fact more talk than action. There is too much ether or hot air!

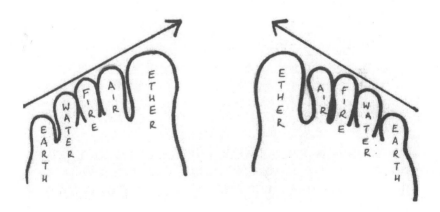

Toe shape, size and position

Toes leaning towards the big toe are thoughts projected to the past.

Toes leaning towards the 5th toe are thoughts projected to the future.

Twisted toes show that the initial energy is presented differently when it meets the outside world. For example, a twisted 2nd toe on the right foot will belong to someone who may find they receive the most inappropriate gifts because people find it difficult to discern what they actually want.

Gaps between toes show a need for more time between those energies. A gap between the big toe and 2nd toe shows that the person needs time to think about something before they decide, if they are rushed they often regret the decision they make.

A toe lifting up from the ground belongs to someone who is trying to detach from reality, if it is the big toe they are apt to daydream or float off into fantasy land.

A pointy toe shows a sharp expression, if on the underside of the 4th toe left foot (love toe) it will belong to someone who expresses themselves sharply to those closest to them.

Other examples:

- Hammertoes are where the base of the toe does not completely touch the ground can represent fear, anxiety and tension. It is as if they are fighting for survival.

- 2nd toe longer than 3rd – analyzing and critical of their self.

- 5th toe bent inwards – problems in trusting others, selective hearing however great capacity of concentration.

- Very small 5th toes – a need to be independent and self sufficient from a very early age, no room for fear, extremely motivated.

EXERCISE: HOW DO YOU THINK?

The movement of toes will identify what dominates the thought patterns. You can try this on your self or others.

Wiggle your toes

Observe how they move

In unison? = thoughts are well cohered and ordered

Splay apart? = open minded, lateral thinker

Stuck together or stiff? = oppressed thought patterns

Toe bullies another? = the energy of one toe dominates

Toes reach forwards? = forward thinking, impatience for action

Toes claw? = fear at having to make decisions

Creates cramp? = fear of thoughts being worthy enough to voice

Notice how you feel when you wiggle your toes.

Toe rotation and stretching can help release head tension and congestion caused by too much worrying or excessive thinking.

Basic Foot Reading Sequence

You may like to use this basic sequence while you practice:

1. Ask them to describe their feet to you

2. What are your first impressions

3. Describe the shape and size of feet and arches

4. What are the dominant or less dominant elements

5. Look for differences in the right (masculine) and left (feminine) foot

6. Notice the direction the feet are facing - past/present/future

7. What signs and indicators can you identify

8. Look at the toes

Offer an affirmation card such as an Angel Card to consolidate the Foot Reading.

Foot Reading Advice:

- Always apply care and sensitivity

- Never judge

- Trust your intuition

- Open your heart

- Speak with love

- Enjoy!

The order or sequence in which you read a foot will be determined by intuition. Initially you start with a first impression and lead from that to describe what those feet tell you about the person. It should be a flowing, effortless process often leading to new insights and particular themes that may re-occur throughout the reading.

Use feedback from your Foot Readings to learn appropriate phrases and descriptions, all feet are as unique as the person they belong with, so verbalising what you observe needs to be adapted to convey this appropriately.

A softer approach for a person who is gentle and shy; a more emphatic, direct approach for someone who needs clearer, succinct words. This will present itself via the feet initially and by your first impression of that person. You may find that practicing on family and friends first helps as you will already know certain things about them.

Never assume to know a person completely though even if you live with them or are related to them.

You can express the self through Foot Reading verbally, using written analysis using photographs (see Foot Reading Case Studies) or with colours, patterns and symbols (see Foot Reading Map).

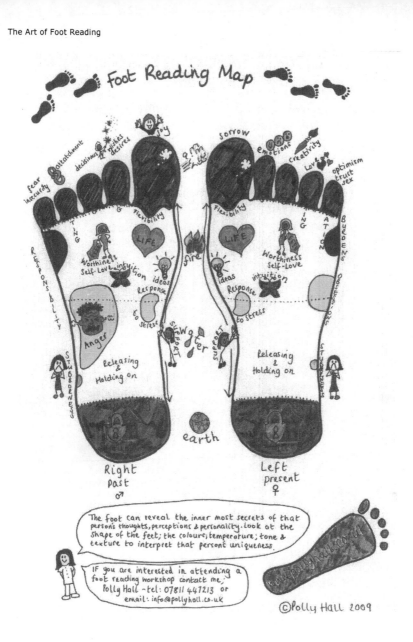

Foot Reading Case Studies

These are in depth analyses of people just by looking at their feet. The Foot Readings were from photographs then the recipients were asked for their feedback. Their comments are written at the end of each reading. I have followed the basic Foot Reading sequence and included headings for ease of reference.

The dates shown are the dates the photographs were taken, so the reading reflect what was current for that person at that time.

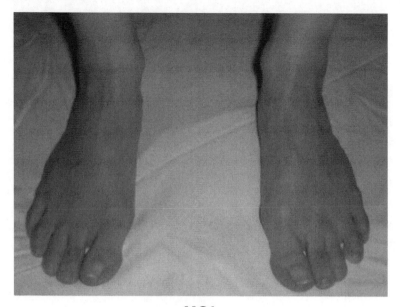

MC1
Date: 20.01.08
Female
Age: 40

First Impressions:

Contrasting aspects of the plantar and dorsal views reveal a distinct difference in how this person views herself and how others perceive her. This person is full of surprises, often hidden aspects of the self are revealed only to those closest to her.

The toes interest me initially as they are individual and deeply original. This person does not conform to any particular group or type, they run their own quest, often to the exclusion of others. The high arches denote solitary independence and a need to feel they are supporting themselves even if in a secure relationship. Hidden potential is shown in the wider shape when viewed from the sole (soul or hidden aspect) compared to the top of the foot, dorsum (what we show to the world, or our face). There is depth of character here.

Elements:

The elements that are dominant are fire and water. The others, earth and air less so. Fire is perhaps the most noticeable, expressing passion or strength in the heart chakra. This person gives out a lot and is highly attractive to those needing comfort or reassurance. It is a healthy, vibrant element capable of taking on heavy burdens, more than they are credited for at times. The water element, or emotional self, shows worry is constant and steady seeping into issues of security, denoted by the earth element or heel. Some anger is resonant in the earth element that may be lying latent from past hurts or issues.

Past/Present/Future:

This person is content with the here and now and feels focused and positive in their actions at this time. The balance is expressed with confidence shown by the space between the two feet.

Signs and Indicators:

What is noticeable on the dorsal side of the foot, is that this person exerts extreme pressure on themselves in order to remain in control. This stretches their thoughts to the limit, lifting them almost to a dreamlike state, a detachment from reality in order to survive.

There are similarities and a balance right now between masculine and feminine aspects, or the logical and intuitive sides of the self. This is good and much needed considering the other conflicting areas.

Healthy colour flows again from the heart area and energy is good here. Some depletion of energy in the rippled instep shows fluctuating emotions having an effect on this system. It is just as well they are in tune with what their physical body needs.

The bulging shoulder reflex area suggests capability to take on responsibility far greater than originally intended. This person can cope with a lot of pressure at any given time and rarely show it externally to the world.

Toes:

This person is hard to fathom, often an enigma and rarely worked out by others. They will repel those unable to cope with this strength of character and attract similar enlightened beings and also stable, earthy types who enjoy a challenge.

They can be argumentative and stubborn when expressing their will, sometimes fruitlessly, but it will make them feel happier because they will have fulfilled their purpose just by expressing it. If unable to express it, they will feel frustrated and resort to self-evaluation which may lead to obsessive and controlling behaviour.

Thoughts are projected to the future and take a slow process, often bottlenecking or stalling before surprising them with the suddenness or explosion into reality. Procrastination twinned with power is an exhausting combination largely because it is like containing an atomic bomb in a walnut shell.

They constantly question their thoughts which puts pressure on how they feel, often draining them physically and mentally. Wishes and desires are straightforward and direct, this person knows what they want and also knows what they need to achieve it. This can cause friction because this certainty is not always shared by those around them.

Relationships to possessions is tied in with work ethic; they like to treat themselves but feel a need to have earned it rather than just be given it. They retain possessions because of a subconscious need that it can make them feel better, but will make a decision, then detach from this and then make extreme changes in their physical environment. This is a case of starting something with such energy that it burns out too quickly to achieve completion, or is unfinished because it does not meet their high standards.

Like a firework, this person bursts forth with energy and enthusiasm then fizzles out. A case of too many ideas and not enough time. They rarely show their insecurities, again hiding behind their complex, chameleon like nature. In fact, there is no need for them to even express fear because most would perceive them as being fearless anyway.

Emotions and creativity are one unit. They feel happiest when making something whether it is a healthy meal or a crocheted scarf. They need to know how things fit together. The simplicity of such basic actions brings contentment. But this solidarity between feeling and acting can result in stubbornness and if they want to do something they will do it to its death rather than change tack. Contrary to this they will also be a difficult person to budge if they have set their mind on something they do not want to do. The decision comes only from them.

There is a more distinct gap between their creating toe and their relationship toe on the left foot, showing that they don't depend on people to source their ideas. Single-mindedness here. It comes from within rather than without. They dwell on the past though and reflect often on past relationships but with a sense of detachment and control. It is as if this toe does not belong to this foot. It would not bother them if they lived as a hermit for the rest of their lives.

The relationship toe also overshadows the love toe and again it is hidden from view. Trust comes hard to this person particularly where people are concerned. They have learnt long and hard lessons through close relationships but hide this well.

They feel that if they were to display the hidden love as wholesomely as it is displayed in the hidden (sole) part of the foot, they would attract too many people who may take their energy away. This would not happen, as 'like attracts like' and they hold ample love for many. Releasing the fear would dispel this perception. It is their perception that hinders them not their intrinsic nature.

Conclusion:

Words to sum up this person include:

Stubborn	Reflective	Perceptive
Complicated	Argumentative	Strong
Independent	Deep	Passionate
Controlling	Soul-searcher	Generous

MC says:

"...did you really do that just from my feet?... it's all completely spot on. You've summed up my life's experiences just by studying my feet; you're a genius! Oh, and it's reminded to work on that stubbornness (amongst other things!)"

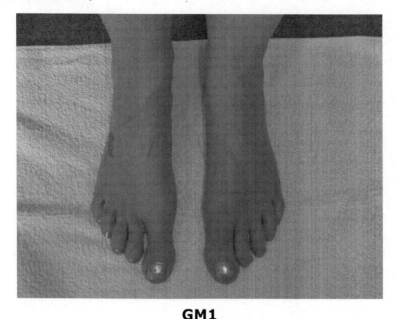

GM1

Date: 10.05.08

Female

Age: 56

First Impressions:

What long straight feet! This person will find it difficult to fit in most places. A bold, unique character with a radical perspective and quirky ideas. They have definitely got more organised than they used to be. A methodical organisation that has served them well in ordering their hectic thoughts.

Elements:

This foot is an airy foot. Filled with ideas and the need to get out there and show the world. It is expansive but in the sense that it reaches to the heavens looking for answers. This person will seek many different spiritual pathways and be very interested in people's beliefs and philosophies. The element that looks in need of most nourishment is 'water'. The earth element has taken on some of the fire element as if they try to ground themselves by draining it down through the head, this is a difficult process and one that can lead to strong fluctuations in mood.

Past/Present/Future:

A more relaxed attitude now than in the past. A lot of self-development work has taken place but still a pressing forward and perceived lack of time to fit in all the plans. On track in the present moment though and positive.

Signs and Indicators:

In the past they were subject to a harsh regime and perhaps strict, principled upbringing that could have led to a tendency to daydream.

The tattoo of a red rose is a symbol of love but again connected to the masculine side (right foot). I expect this was done at a time when they were feeling more content at displaying their individuality. The position of the rose shows it is given as a gift back to the self.

The red marks/scars on the inner ankle, perhaps caused by restricted footwear show a need to be free, anything that appears to put pressure on this person will create friction and sometimes be a painful experience.

I think this person has had to rein in their ambitious nature most of their life, and although they like to perform, their perceptions of themselves has been pressured by what others say about them.

In the past, two very distinct traumas had had an impact on this person and although parallel in intensity they relate to two different events. This person finds it difficult to receive help and external guidance which can result in some festering anger if it is not forthcoming, particularly as they are naturally intuitive and don't understand when others cannot see what is going on.

Toes:

Radical, individual thoughts and perceptions. An expressive, bold verbaliser and difficult to stop once this person gets going. They talk at length about what they believe in and their ideas. If this was harnessed they would achieve a great deal. In the past there was a stalling of energy here as if the process could not be rushed – a bottleneck in the thinking process which once passed would then explode into being. It's just as well this person has nice rounded toes or the force of her verbalisations would be dramatic. This person has become more aware of this power in the present and lets her emotions impact on the thought process.

It is clear to this person what they want but others may be confused by them. I would not be surprised if this person receives really inappropriate gifts where someone else has totally misunderstood what they asked for.

Also, they will be certain about what has been decided but they show others they need more time. Decisions are based on past experience and it's unlikely they will forget if something has made them angry.

There is conflict here with material possessions. On the one side they strongly believe that what's inside a person is the value of their worth, yet they adore 'nice things' and will surround themselves with them. This is justified especially if the objects have spiritual significance or meaning. I would like to see where this person lives as I'd imagine lots of decoration and sparkle with vibrant colours.

They try to hide their fear and insecurities and often can make themselves feel better if they get dressed up and pampered. Emotions are kept on hold and manipulated to a time when it's appropriate. More impulsive now than in the past. Creativity is abundant but kept hidden, perhaps out of modesty because they have been told to 'stop showing off' early on in life.

Again there is no pretence in this person's mind as to what constitutes a good relationshiop, referring to past experiences. They are private about relationships though and keep this very much to themselves.

They also appear to rely on others but show a deep need for trust in any interaction.

Words to sum up this person include:

Vibrant	Quirky	Explosive
Ambitious	Free-spirited	Private
Verbal	Radical	Modest
Philosophical	Changeable	Dreamer

GM1 says:

"Thank you for that foot reading it was absolutely fab!

I found this reading to be extremely interesting and spot on a lot of the reading. I do however fit in places but normally only stay for a short while. I have definitely got more organised and methodical through my life. This is because I do have a busy life (my own choosing) and I have to organise my hectic thoughts.

I love my red rose tattoo and had this done not long after I got divorced from my husband – having found my individual identity again. I call myself a free spirit, and wear a lot of open shoes not restricting so my big toe can breathe!

I feel I am ambitious and I get quite frustrated when things do not happen. I have had a couple of traumas and I do find it difficult to accept help, being very independent and resourceful. Being intuitive is also very true and cannot understand why other people cannot see the obvious.

Radical, individual thoughts and perceptions are very true of me and my decisions are made on past recollections. I never forget anything that has made me angry, probably forgive, but will never encounter that again.

Very true on the material possessions, I believe in inner beauty but I adore pretty sparkly quality possessions being either of spiritual significance, crystals or even antique or art décor.

I enjoy my wardrobe and change weekly my look from tailored suits to floaty gypsy skirts – enjoy being pampered – but also give holistic treatments occasionally. I have a lot of creative skills but feel that I am modest.

The words that have been summed up for me would be fairly accurate. Thank you Polly for an amazing reading."

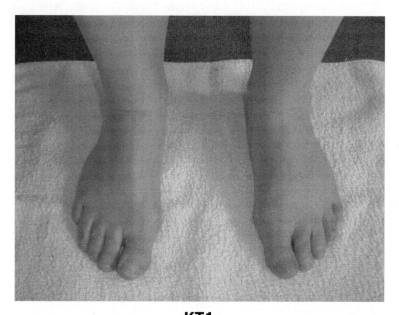

KT1

Date: 10.05.08

Female

Age: 47

First Impressions:

This person doesn't hang about waiting for something to be done. They will jump straight in and get on with it. No airs and graces, they call a spade a spade and will not tolerate idleness. They might stomp straight in sometimes without thinking but they mean well so no damage is done.

This person rarely sits down to contemplate life but will find relaxation in a more active way like going for a long walk or getting out in the garden. They are happy to suss others out before revealing themselves. Good at blending in the background. This person prefers the company of others around them but can work independently as well as being sociable.

This person likes to do a task in the right way, a methodical approach.

Elements:

Most definitely an earthy foot all over, broad and capable of taking on activities. This is reflected in the solidness of the tone, it is rare for this person to be knocked by others as they will stand their ground. In fact they are well grounded and will feel strongest when connected to the earth element in nature. They will love autumn when the energy is drawn back into the earth and will feel at their most creative then.

Another element that shows as having an impact is fire which tries to brush down the earth element. This person naturally harnesses her passions so they don't overthrow her.

Past/Present/Future:

This person is on track and focused on the present moment. Although they will be ready to leap from the couch the moment we are finished.

Signs and Indicators:

Some friction lately on her perceptions of people and possessions. This is linked with support offered to this person recently and feeling vulnerably about being self-sufficient.

This person is a born worrier but won't feel they can trouble others or ask for help. Because they are so well grounded they just get on with it and protect themselves by keeping on the go.

This person has had some difficulty expressing her feelings and has on several occasions had to swallow difficult life experiences. Others may see this person as strong-willed and stubborn.

Toes:

A helpful person who puts others first, will be found in a caring role but needs to watch their back. They are feeling this more now and the amount of time and energy given to others has created some friction especially on the emotions.

This person plans and looks to the future, forward thinking and organising. A list maker I expect who will constantly cross things off and add new with something else always cropping up.

Thoughts put pressure on feelings especially when this person stops for a moment. They tell themselves they will feel better about things tomorrow or in a while, there is also a tendency for wishful thinking here. The stubbornness shows again with the 2nd/3rd toe being closely connected. This person comes across as needing time to make a decision but actually they have already made it but bide their time giving the impression they need to think about it.

They like to reflect on their past and the things they had then. In fact they will reminisce about the good times in the past and hold onto items that have special significance. They appear to not show fear or insecurity however if personal belongings are attacked they will feel this as a personal slight on themselves.

They prefer to undertake projects where they see a clear completion happening and will lose interest if things don't come to fruition as quickly as they'd like. Something like embroidery would drive them mad because they'd have to sit still and wouldn't complete it all in one go.

When they look back to the past they are inclined to say their relationships were stronger, maybe with friends. This person has had to look after their own interests from an early age. Love and trust are paramount and probably mean the same thing to this person. Love equals trust. Trust equals love.

Conclusion:

There is no way this person will slow down but they can be more aware by incorporating stillness into their daily life. They are strong and honest so will be a sturdy friend to those who offer respect. Look out anyone who decides to cross this person. There is a lethal combination of fire (passion) and earth (strength).

Words to sum up this person include:

Strong	Grounded	Helpful
Doer	Worrier	Earthy
Organiser	Stubborn	Sociable
Worker	Strong-willed	Approachable

KT1 says:

"Wow! I think your reading very much reflects my true self. The only exception I would make is to say that I don't believe I'm a born worrier (anymore) I have learnt to put things in perspective more. It was good to see these things about me written down – it's as though they are confirming what I felt about myself but hadn't really believed it. Great stuff."

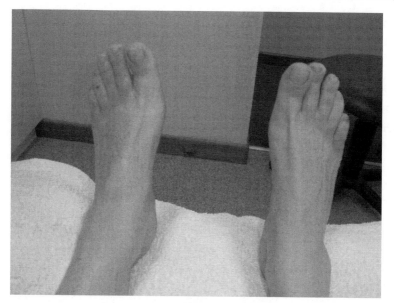

SC1

Date: 09.05.08

Female

Age: 65

First Impressions:

The colours of the feet are noticeably different on plantar and dorsal aspects suggesting that the emotions of this person are often kept hidden. There is a strong independence of spirit here and pressure put on the self to succeed. The right foot appears more tense suggesting a resistance to masculine traits in the self and in life. This foot also shows past influences and a stricter philosophy adhered to in the past than now. These feet say 'I am here to help you', upright and assertive and capable of facing the world, good and bad.

Elements:

On first inspection this person shows they are well balanced in the four elements of air, fire, water and earth. But I would suggest that fire is slightly dominant shown in the expansion on the ball of the foot. Earth and fire work well together. This person can get passionate about things close to her heart but still retain a grounded perspective also. There is contained, latent anger in the fact that this person has had to take on burdens, perceived to be unshared equally by others. The water element appears most depleted suggesting a draining in emotions especially recently. As if the plug has been pulled out and she can now let go.

Past/Present/Future:

This person feels well balanced and focused on the present moment right now. There is confidence in the large space between the two feet and uprightness of their position. A positive outlook.

Signs and Indicators:

This person puts pressure on themselves to do well and this shows more in the past foot. Fluctuating changes in mood are kept hidden from others and are quite subtle. This person invests emotionally in different spiritual pathways and goes with what feels right with a natural intuition. There is a change in thought patterns; in the past the head ruled the heart mostly but this has been balanced later in life and the head does not put as much pressure on the feelings now.

There is softness which is hidden from view and most people would imagine this person to be quite dry and serious. However, the vibrancy and fun is there but only shown to those who know her deeply.

The slight bunions on both feet show a need to help others, this shows more in the past (right foot) where it could have been to the detriment of this person. 'Bending over backwards' to help is a phrase that springs to mind and could manifest physically as back problems.

Toes:

Thoughts are expressed tactfully but often about the future. A person who plans and organises for future events. These are difficult to read thought patterns as they are so well hidden from view. This person may appear elusive to others and rarely gives anything away too much especially to strangers.

When active this person lets their intellect and learnt knowledge put pressure on their feelings. It almost overshadows it which can create a lot of tension in the head area. A lot of modesty here although they would probably deny this.

The shorter big toe shows someone who is ideal in a support role, a multi-tasker able to think of twenty things and do ten all at the same time.

What is interesting is the perspective from which the toes are observed. This person's perspective on life is clear to them but conveyed very differently to outsiders. Decisions appear straightforward to this person but others may see a laboured thinking process with eventual explosion of action. A real burst of energy once a decision is finalised. There is a short amount of time needed before action is taken. Impulsive people will find this person's calm, collected manner quite frustrating but that is their problem.

Dreams and wishes can materialise as much larger than originally conceived. The creativity is hidden from view and linked to material things, there is a love of beauty and art here but not necessarily coming from the person but an appreciation of what already has been created. Nostalgia here is shown by the 4th toes leaning to the past. This person can get sentimental about objects that have meaning to them. Equally they can be quite harsh with their attachments and de-clutter or clear out lots in one go once a decision to start fresh is made.

This person appears fearless to others, a great person to be around in a crisis or emergency. They will express when they are not feeling secure about something so there is no doubt and even on occasions make it appear that they are more afraid just to make someone else feel better. This can hanker at their thoughts because if there's one thing this person can't stand, it's inauthentic or fake behaviour. Falseness just does not wash and they will soon suss out if someone is genuine or not.

There is less pressure put on feelings now than in the past. In the past there was a necessity to draw in the reins and not let emotions be overwhelmed. Now it is as if a pact has been made between thoughts and feelings and a maturation of these two sometimes conflicting aspects of self.

This person is good at expressing how they feel and with kindness, which is good in many ways especially if they have to express things that don't want to be heard by a third party. A diplomat – who would be mortified if they felt they had upset someone with their words.

Conclusion:

They are happiest when doing something they enjoy, there is no point in pursuing something if no pleasure can be gained. Other people put pressure on them particularly recently and this has led to a depletion in core energy. A perceived attack on how current relationships affect them is difficult to comprehend because this person selflessly acts for others (although may deny this as being a rare trait because it comes naturally to them). They know when to trust and when not to, more from an in-built trait than from learned experience. Their tendency to bend to please others can result in some vulnerability here but this is managed well.

Words to sum up this person include:

Tactful	Helpful	Diplomatic
Selfless	Independent	Calm
Private	Responsible	Assertive
Grounded	Spirited	Caring

SC says:

"Very true about keeping my emotions hidden. I've always had strong feelings. Still feel very depleted and continue to worry. Not sure about positive outlook as I still feel negative about life. I've not been able to express feelings in the past which has carried on and I am very sensitive when people do not see me as this, I try to hide the fact and appear strong. I will always help anybody in any way I can. Once I've made my mind up I will not change. I do make my mind up about people on first impressions. I always tried to please others to get praise which was something I never got whilst growing up."

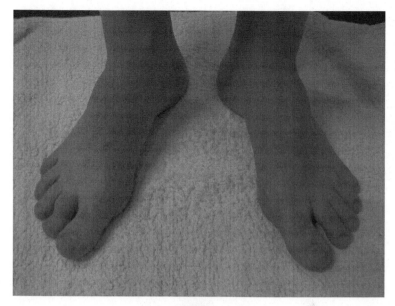

SS1

Date: 20.06.08

Male

Age: 40

First Impressions:

The position of these feet are different depending on which perspective their viewed so it's likely that not many people know this person's true self. The left (present) pushes forward, showing an impatience to get on with life and move away from past ways of being. This is less evident when viewed from the outside (dorsal aspect), so what is shown to the world is a much less confident person than is felt on the inside. Many will be surprised by this person's achievements as it is not clear at first glance. There is a vibrancy and passion hidden beneath the surface often reserved for close friends and it's likely that it will be missed by others.

Elements:

There is a balance of elements here but predominantly air and water showing strong mental capacity linked with gut instinct and inner knowing. A successful combination provided the earth element or ability to stay grounded and focused holds all these characteristics in check. The fire element appears vibrant and glowing, lots of energy invested in this person's hearts desire and manifestation of dreams and wishes in a creative sense.

Past/Present/Future:

This person feels as if the past no longer serves them, in fact it has become a bit of a burden and can drag them down a bit. This leads to an over-emphasis on what is wanted in the future and a looking forward to changes which are perceived to be positive. Anything is seen as better than the status quo which is rather neglected in the extensive planning and mulling over of endless possibilities.

Signs and Indicators:

This person is a secret worrier and doesn't show it openly. It manifests more likely as irritation or pressure put on self. They believe they are totally responsible for their actions and will openly admit their mistakes, expecting others to also have this high degree of integrity and openness.

They are self-disciplined in some areas of their life but can be reckless in others. For example, in terms of health the digestive area shows a weakness and harmful bouts of indulgence, used as a comfort substitute to counterbalance worry is not particularly good for them.

The high arches indicate a strong independent streak, almost a loner in some respects with self-reliance of high importance to them. They see new challenges as a way to demonstrate their capabilities, whether personal or professional and thrive where they need to meet the demands of others.

Recently there has been some reflection on feelings about work which has put pressure on them and this is being verbalised more and more. What is not shown is the potential build up of resentment that is likely to manifest if this person does not act.

Toes:

What is noticeable is the tension in the toes differing when this person is relaxed and active. They find it easy to relax and switch thoughts to another mode but when working they keep a tight grip as if like a coiled spring ready to react.

This person is an adaptor, they will make themselves fit into almost any situation or environment; socially, vocationally, culturally, and adapt their responses and expressions to suit. This is more developed with the ability to manipulate wishes and desires to suit what will work best for them. They refer to past decisions and can instantly reflect on ways of improving. When making decisions concerning their private life they need a bit more time to mull things over but when in a work environment, they are self-disciplined and decisive.

They have had to restrict their grand ideas to fit to an externally imposed mould. This could be limiting thoughts from an early age that they try hard to break free from. This hampers their way of expressing things to others and they may have learned to not be so blunt based on others reactions to them.

They have a love of material things that hold significance or meaning in some way but are not materialistic. These attachments will be to a memory, place or person. They hide any fearfulness, tucking it out of the way and any insecurity is kept close to their chest.

There may be misunderstandings in terms of decisions made where they are clear on their part but others may misconstrue what is meant. This feeling of being misunderstood is a self-perception and can lead to stubbornness or force of will expressed by them believing they are right.

They express themselves in a nice, rounded way. They will say it how it is with no pretension which may upset less direct, more sensitive people.

They can sometimes appear clumsy or insensitive but have tried to change their way of interacting with others in order to have a better perception of themselves. Because they are not often phased by others behaviour they do not think their actions will have such a huge effect. When put under pressure they will follow a strategic, methodical plan of action that is carefully calculated and precise. This is learned behaviour and they would ideally like to be impulsive and spontaneous.

Something has dented their optimist streak and they tend to classify people into like/don't like, trust/don't trust which to all purposes is the same thing to them.

They are extremely generous with their time and affection more than is initially anticipated. Some may regard them as over familiar but this is because they are sure of others motivations and will display a lot of trust almost immediately to those they like.

Words to sum up this person include:

Friendly	Structured	Responsible
Independent	Worrier	Adaptable
Under-estimated	Assertive	Precise
In control	Open-minded	Stubborn

SS1 says:

"By and large I think the reading was fairly accurate. I am definitely impatient and a vibrant and passionate person! I have a 'different' future than the classical career one that has been mapped out over the years. I do tend to worry until I have worked a problem through to my satisfaction. I am self-disciplined as the reading suggested and independent. I am also an 'adaptor' and not materialistic as observed in the reading. Thank you for a surprisingly accurate reading which I enjoyed."

A – Z Index of Common Foot Conditions

Looking at the physical areas affected the foot can be read by presenting condition on an emotional level. Use the symbol key below to identify which parts of the foot are associated and what it means emotionally.

SYMBOLS KEY:

Toes = t

Nails = n

Dorsal = d

Plantar = p

Skin = s

Bones = x

Tendons = te

Ligaments = l

Fluids = f

Ball = b

Instep/arch = ia

Heel = h

CONDITION	PHYSICAL AREAS AFFECTED	FOOT READING ASPECT
Athletes Foot (tinea pedis)	s/t/p	Eating away at self
Blisters	s	Recent irritation bubbling up to the surface
Bunion (hallux valgus)	b/t	Diversion off course of path, doing much for others
Callous (hyperkeratosis)	s	Deep protection of self from perceived external threat
Chilblains (erythema pernio)	s/t/f	Extremes of emotions, going hot and cold, changeable self
Corns (circumscribed hyperkeratosis)	s	Specific irritation wearing deep into self, check exact location
Cramp	te/l	Momentary halting due to sudden subconscious fear
Excessive sweating (hyperhidrosis)	s/f	Fear of unknown, leaking out of unexplored emotions
Fallen arches	ia/x/te/l	Support dropped, sudden need to feel safe by seeking solid ground
Flat Feet (pes planovalgus)	ia/x/te/l	Solidly realistic, sceptical unless provided with facts
Fungal infection	s/n/t	Eating away at self, low self worth

CONDITION	PHYSICAL AREAS AFFECTED	FOOT READING ASPECT
High arch (pes cavus)	ia/x/te/l	Likes to be independent all the time, keeps emotions detached from real life
Ingrown toenail	t/s	Perceptions of thoughts digging away all the time until pain causes a need to act
Malodour (bromohidrosis)	s/f	Unhealthy thoughts and emotions surfacing and causing a stink
Moles	s	Past life or genetic patterns (check size colour and location)
Pain in ball of foot (metatarsalgia)	b/x/te/l	Pressure on how the self is expressed
Pain in heel (calcaneal bursitis)	h/te/l	Pressure on stability, security
Rams horn toe (onchogryphosis)	t/n	Perceived attack on beliefs
Tendonitis	te	Inflexibility, stubbornness to see change is needed
Thickened nails (onychauxis)	t/n	Protection of beliefs by barricading thoughts in
Verrucae (paplioma virus)	s	External influences eating away at own ideas and patterns

More about Foot Reading

Some related sources of information include:

Analyzing Personality Patterns through the Feet by Moshe Kruchik ISBN 965-90709-0-X

Heal Your Body by Louise Hay ISBN 1-870845-04-8

Language of the Feet by Chris Stormer ISBN 0-340-64345-5

Reading Toes – Your Feet as Reflections of your Personality by Imre Somogyi ISBN 0-85207-310-0

Learn more about Foot Reading at a workshop or buy Foot Reading charts online at

www.pollyhall.co.uk

If you would like a detailed personal Foot Reading as shown in the Case Studies section of this book please contact Polly Hall at info@pollyhall.co.uk.

Glossary

Chakra	energy centre of which the main seven are identified on the chakra foot map
Contraindication	a reason for not carrying out treatment e.g. broken bones
Dorsal	the top part of the foot
Elements	relates to air, fire, water and earth
Intuition	an inner knowing or feeling
Lateral	the outer edge of the foot
Longitudinal arch	the arch that runs from the big toe to the inner heel
Medial	the inner edge of the foot
Plantar	the sole part of the foot
Reflex area	a part of the foot specifically linked with another part of the body e.g. brain reflex area is on the big toes
Signs and indicators	the markings and physical identifiers found on the feet e.g. colour, texture, temperature
Transverse arch	the arch across the width of the foot